nailclass

award winning advice for the serious technician

written by gigi rouse

personal notes

FOREWORD

A chance comment by one of the members of www.thenailgeek.com (the largest online community for nail professionals in the world) led me to start a series of tutorials to help nail technicians with problems related to techniques used when creating nail enhancements.

By and large, skillful, efficient techniques for working are not learned on nail courses. There's simply too much information overload on a student at the beginning stages for him or her to take in the subtle nuances that expert technique requires. It can take many years to develop the necessary proficiency to make your work stand out from the rest.

This handbook of techniques will help you on your way to becoming the nail artist you aspire to be and will, I hope, reduce the time it would take you to muddle through developing methods on your own.

Many of the techniques in this book are the same as those I've taught to the many competitors who have come to me for help so that they could become winners. Happily, many of them have gone on to do just that and I'm proud to have played a little part in their success.

gigi

Gigi Rouse

DEDICATION

I dedicate this book to Samuel Sweet (THE Nail Geek), whose idea to start an online teaching forum for nail professionals, where they could find unbiased, truthful and factual information, was the inspiration that led to its creation.

My thanks go to all the Nail Geeks who urged me to get on and just 'do it'.

Most notably: Mrs. Geek, Lell, Tracey UK, NailsinLondon1, Dawnie, Jeni Giles, joannerowsell, SassyHassy, Karren, Aspirations, Inspirationails, mum, Nails@42ndstreet, Glorsclaws, Anna from Toronto, Tickled Pink, emmam, Groovynails, Scattyfox, Ruby, JCS, Cuticles, Jaydee, and Globalgal.

I am also grateful for the support from many others on the site who added their encouragement.

Grateful thanks also to all my winners! They're the ones who have taken the information, dedicated themselves to their art and put the magic into their work, none more so than the unbeatable Ketan Patel.

CONTENTS

CHAPTER 1: Perfect Preparation Prevents Poor Performance

It doesn't matter whether you're redecorating your home or replanting your garden, making a dress or baking a cake. Whatever task you set out to accomplish, the better your preparation, the easier and better the job will be, the better it will look and the longer it will last.

Lack of thorough preparation is the cause of 99% of the 'lifting' technicians see in the salon. Even when technicians tell me, "I know my preparation is perfect," if they're suffering from lifting on a regular basis, I know it isn't!

Preparation is one part of the nail service that cannot and must not be rushed. Thorough PREP will take the most time of any part of the whole service; application and finishing will take much less time proportionally.

Preparation is all about removing cuticle from the nail plate.

There's much confusion as to just what cuticle is. It's referred to as true cuticle, non-living tissue, pterygium, and probably many more things. All of them are misleading. Some people think the cuticle is the eponychium. Let's define it now.

Cuticle is made up of exfoliated skin cells from the folds of skin surrounding the nail unit.

Cuticle is non-living.

Cuticle is not pterygium (which is an overgrowth of skin cells).

Cuticle is not the eponychium (which is the living skin surrounding the base of the nail unit). And cuticle isn't 'true cuticle' as opposed to false cuticle - it is cuticle.

If the cuticle isn't regularly removed or rubbed off in some way, it builds and sticks together until it looks almost like a membrane growing from under the eponychium. But it's not growing and it's not living. It's just building up until it's removed.

Always use a hand sanitiser on yourself and your client before you start the full set procedure - or any procedure. We will assume here that you're preparing for a full set of nail enhancements.

First, take a good look at the overall condition of the client's hands and nails. Chances are, if they're coming to you for the first time, the nails will have been neglected. Nails that haven't been regularly manicured will have a large build-up of cuticle on the nail plate (even if you can't see it) which will have to be removed gently and thoroughly before any enhancement products are applied. Otherwise, there will be a barrier between the product and the plate, which will cause the product to separate from the plate. In a word, lifting.

Lifting is something you don't want your clients to experience. Lifting is the root of many problems for the technician. It leads to clients picking at the product and can lead to a bacterial infection as well as being an unsightly breakdown of service that won't encourage clients to carry on with regular maintenance of their nails.

Removing lifted product is time consuming and stressful to both the product and the natural nail as well as to the technician and the client.

The good news is that lifting doesn't need to happen at all as long as you're performing perfect preparation, using good application techniques and, of course, choosing a good product line.

Once you have a general idea of the condition of your client's nails, apply an excellent quality cuticle remover to each nail plate and give it a minute to get working. If you rush right in and start to remove the cuticle build-up, you'll find that the last nails you work on are much more thoroughly prepared than the first ones because the remover has had more time to work. This is one reason we often see more lifting on clients' right hands than left hands. So be patient for a minute, and the difference will be marked.

Using a disinfected metal pusher, if you can and if it's comfortable for the client, gently push back the eponychium to expose the maximum amount of nail plate. If the eponychium does not want to move, then don't force it.

Next, use the pusher to loosen and lift all cuticle from the plate. If there's a lot of build-up, you may need to use more cuticle remover. Sometimes it's also necessary to use a disinfected pair of cuticle nippers and actually nip away the 'membrane' that's formed from beneath the eponychium. Be very careful never to nip any living tissue when performing this procedure.

Please don't be tempted to 'shortcut' gentle removal by using an abrasive to file away the cuticle from the plate.

Many technicians do this to the detriment of the health of the nail plate and, eventually, to the detriment of the enhancements and, finally, even to the detriment of their own business. We all know that the healthier the nail plate, the stronger and more lasting the enhancements will be. I don't know of any client who would enter a salon knowing that the technician was going to ruin the condition of her nails. Clients expect us to be responsible for the good health of their nails, and as professionals we must all meet that challenge.

Once you've removed every trace of cuticle from the plate, the rest is easy. Using a soft nail buffer, and working in a north/south direction from the eponychium to the free edge (the direction of nail growth), do your final exfoliation.

Never work back and forth with the buffer, but only in one direction. I always say, 'Once with the buffer exfoliates the nail. Ahhh! Twice thins the nail. Ouch!' Make sure you get into the nail grooves, as this is an area where debris can be trapped.

Finally, using a lint-free pad and a sanitising solution, remove all traces of cuticle and dust from the surface of the plate. Really scrub the plate well and get into all the nail grooves: just wiping is not enough. Let dry. The nail plate is now perfectly prepared for perfect product application.

CHAPTER 2: Choosing the Correct Length for Balance and Beauty

We all know the expression, 'Beauty is in the eye of the beholder', but this statement is subject to debate regarding nails.

There are times in creating nail enhancements when we need to be a bit more disciplined and apply 'rules of design' in order to please our clients or competition judges.

It's even more important to understand that the rules need to change a little bit when we're using the French application of whatever product we choose. When the tips of the nails are whiter-than-white, it tends to distort the balance of the overall look and can easily make an enhancement look top-heavy and ungainly.

I judge many technicians' work, in competitions and - even more often - in the photographs they submit to me for critiques. Most of the time, the technical work or the application of the product is excellent. The thing that most often lets a technician's work down, in my eyes, is that the length they've chosen is just too long and the symmetry and balance of the finished work isn't as attractive as it could be and would have been if only the free edge had been made shorter.

Many technicians are inspired by competition winners' work, but it must be emphasised that the criteria for competition nails is unrealistic in the salon; they are two separate areas of expertise.

In competition work, technicians produce an 'extreme' smile line in order to 'strut their stuff' and show the judges the consistent control they have when using their white product to create these lines.

Although this extreme look can be used successfully on a model whose nail beds are extremely long, it can actually foreshorten the look of a normal or shorter-than-average nail bed length, making the nails less attractive. The same thing applies, of course, to salon clients: a natural smile line shape (which accounts for 99% of cases) will be more attractive unless the client has ultra-long nail beds.

Barring the odd instance where a client is 'extreme' and likes to break all the rules, below are the rules for the prettiest look and the most practical 'real life' length.

The free edge of the enhancement should never be longer than half the length of the nail bed. The length can, of course, be anything shorter than this length that compliments the hand of the client or model.

When using the French Look with a brilliant white free edge, the rule should be altered to:

- the free edge of the enhancement should be just a bit shorter than half the length of the nail bed
- making the enhancements just that tiny bit, or more, shorter, creates the perfect combination of balance and beauty for which we all strive.

CHAPTER 3: Brush Control Part 1- Getting a Grip

Even though the brush is a nail technician's primary tool, many people have never worked with a brush prior to becoming nail technicians. Maybe that's why they don't take the brush seriously enough.

Doing nails well is an art form. It is not just a mechanical task. But many people never move beyond the mechanical to the higher form of art. Why? Because they never really learn the fundamentals of working with a brush, or, better yet, of how to make their brush work for them.

A brush is a tool, pure and simple.

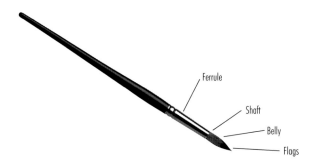

Ferrule

Shaft

Belly

Flags

Working with different parts of a brush produces different effects. There is a flat side, a round side, a point and a belly - all have different functions and all produce different effects on the bead of product you create with your brush. Different pressures on different parts of the brush also produce different effects.

So it's paramount that, if you're going to make that brush an extension of yourself and make it do what you want it to do and produce what you want to produce, you have to know how it works inside and out and feel totally comfortable and fluent with it.

First, you just have to know how to hold it! It has to feel as comfortable and as easy in your fingers as holding a pen.

You're going to grip the brush with only the thumb, index and middle fingers (just as you would hold any writing implement). Pick up the brush and pretend you're writing your name with it. In fact, do just that: write your name with it while it's dry.

Did that feel comfortable? Are you holding the brush too far back?

Move your fingers up to the metal part of the brush (the ferrule), grip it there and try again. Chances are this feels more comfortable and is more like your normal pen grip. Also notice how you're nicely balanced on your forearm and the heel of your hand as you write.

Once you get a grip on your brush, it's vital that you always hold and use it in the same manner. In this way, your brush will become 'trained' to your way of working. Never loan a trained brush to anyone else to use; it's far too personal an item to pass around the salon.

Balance is another key to working effectively with your brush.

You can't work fluently with your brush if you're balanced on the heel of your hand - it's too restricting. You have to balance on something else instead while you work. It's impossible to do artwork if your brush hand isn't balanced on something. I often see students and beginners struggling to produce a smile line while their hand and arm are in mid-air! It just can't be done. Balance is the key.

Think about how you apply nail polish on another person. You don't do it with your hand in mid-air! Most of us naturally balance on a finger of our other hand (the hand that's holding the client's finger). You do exactly the same thing when using your brush to apply a bead made of liquid and powder or gel. In case this explanation doesn't click, I'll explain what I mean.

A nail technician should only ever use three digits of each hand when working: the thumb, index and middle finger of one's left hand for holding the client's finger, and the thumb, index and middle finger of one's right hand for holding the brush. (The opposite for lefties.) No other digits should ever be needed for holding. This nicely leaves the ring and pinkie finger of each hand to rest on each other for balance.

Find what is the most comfortable position for you. It could be resting your pinkie finger on the pinkie finger of the other hand or resting the pinkie on the ring finger or whatever, as long as your hand is balanced and not waving about in the breeze, leaving your three other fingers to use and work with the brush.

As you work with your brush, you'll be doing a variety of things with it. It's not all brushing! In fact, there is very little actual brushing done when applying nail products.

You will be:
- pressing or patting
- smoothing or stroking
- pushing or pulling
- nudging
- detailing or perfecting

All of the time - for each individual movement - you'll be turning or altering the angle of the brush in your three fingers as you work (more about this in Part 3).

The brush doesn't remain static in one position. You must learn to be very fluid and easy as you work with a brush. How fluid you become will absolutely determine how round and beautiful and natural-looking the finished overlay you create will be.

CHAPTER 4: Brush Control Part 2 - Using the Parts of the Brush and Getting the Angle

You may think all brushes are the same, but they're not.

Never try to save money by buying brushes for doing nails at an art store! Brushes for doing nails differ from art store brushes in several respects. Most art store brushes are made of squirrel hair, which is much too soft for working with the materials we use in our business.

The weight of the bead alone would make the hairs bend and no 'snap' or pressure can be created with a squirrel brush. Even if you find a brush made of firmer material, art store brushes use glue for holding the hairs in the brush, which is often dissolved by the monomer liquid used in making nail enhancements. There is nothing more irritating than hairs coming out of your brush and getting into your work.

The handles of art store brushes aren't finished in a material that can withstand exposure to monomer liquid and they become sticky and unsightly. So use the correct tools for the job you're doing. Good brushes cost money; there is no cheap option for your most important tool.

Kolinsky sable is the preferred hair chosen for nail brushes because it has the perfect amount of snap and resilience to work a bead of acrylic into place. You'll want a brush that's hand-tied and not glued into the ferrule of the brush so there's less chance of contamination of your monomer liquid or of the brush falling apart as long as it's cared for correctly. A good-quality brush that's looked after properly will last a good year even in a busy business.

Kolinsky sable brushes have a characteristic dark portion at the end of each hair and this dark portion is known as the 'flags' of the brush. It is only the flags that we use to pat, push, press or smooth the acrylic beads. (Note: if you use gel products, the brushes are completely different and will be explained in a later chapter along with different techniques.)

The belly portion of the brush (located behind the flags) is the part of the hairs that hold and dispense the liquid into the bead. You will never need to use the belly to press the acrylic bead. Using the belly portion of the brush is unwieldy, unnecessary, and can cause liquid monomer to slop onto the skin, which can lead to over-exposure and eventual allergy. I know that some educators teach to use the belly of the brush. If you've been taught that way, try to unlearn this habit. You can produce much finer quality work by using a brush in the correct way.

The ferrule, or metal portion, of the brush houses the shaft of the hairs.

A brush can be used with the hairs flattened, like a paddle, or rounded and to a fine point, depending on what you want to achieve with it. Pressing or patting is done with the brush hairs flattened like a paddle.

Smoothing or stroking is done with the brush hairs flattened like a paddle.

Pushing or pulling is done with the brush hairs flattened like a paddle.

Nudging is done with the side of a flattened brush or with the fine point of the brush.

Detailing or perfecting is done with the fine point of the brush.

MANOEUVRING THE BRUSH TO CREATE ART
Getting the Right Angle: Angle Number 1

Many of you may quite naturally do many of the things suggested, in which case, move on. But for many to whom brushes and how they work is pretty foreign territory, I suggest that you read slowly and carefully, trying to visualise and digest each segment of information before moving on to the next segment. Otherwise, what is simple will seem complicated.

The angle created between the brush and the nail is crucial in determining the way your product moves.

The angle is created in two different ways or a combination of both ways:
- you hold the finger in one position and raise or lower the handle of your brush, or,
- you hold the brush in one position and raise or lower the finger, or,
- you use a combination of the two movements.

How you create the angle between the brush and the nail isn't important; what is important is that you do not create the wrong angle and spoil your work. For example, if the finger is too low or the brush handle is too high, you're going to create a sharp angle. If this happens, the bead of product you place on the nail is going to be 'scooped up' by the brush and deposited further toward the free edge as you work, creating a thick, barrel-shaped and very unattractive nail enhancement. To create gentle curves and natural looking enhancements, the movements must be subtle and no drastic angles should be used.

Maybe a good way in which to visualise the relationship between brush angle and product is to think of a beach where the sand is all lovely and smooth and flat. If you gently stroke your hand flat along the sand, you won't disturb it very much. But if you raise the flat of your hand up off the sand, creating an angle, and just use your fingers, you'll scoop the sand along, building up a pile and disturbing the smooth surface.

Experiment with your brush and some product on tips and see how changing the angle affects what you do.

So, adopting the correct balance plus a gentle angle between the brush and the nail will make your work much easier and the result more beautiful - and that's the goal you're trying to achieve. Create the perfect nail with your brush and then you won't need to do much filing to finish. Remember our mantra: Filing is boring! Work with your brush not your file.

Getting the Right Angle: Angle Number 2

As well as the angle between the brush and the nail, there's another thing to think about, and that's the relationship between the flat side of your brush and the angle of it to the curve of the nail. Sounds complicated? Take one concept at a time and it isn't.

If you stroked the flat side of your brush down the centre of the nail, the whole surface of the brush would be in contact with it, right? But if you kept stroking the brush in the same way and moved a little further to the side of the nail, only half, or even less, of the brush would be touching the surface unless you twisted the brush a little bit to alter the angle of the flat side, so it all stayed in contact with the surface.

What this means is that when you smooth the product from north to south down the length of the nail, at the same time, you also have to twist the brush at each stroke to keep the flat side in contact with the curved surface of the nail. By the time you get to the sidewall of the nail, the flat side of your brush should be at a right angle to the way it was when you started. Doing this ensures that the product doesn't build up and become thick at the sides. If you're a student or a beginner, one of your most common problems may be thick product in the wrong places, which causes your work to be unsightly and to suffer from problems like lifting. Learning about Angles 1 and 2 and how they affect where your product ends up is crucial to becoming an artist and not just a mechanic.

CHAPTER 5: Brush Control Part 3 - The Smile Line

Think of a tennis racquet and how it's used in playing the game. If every tennis player used the racket in just one way and mastered only one stroke, it would be very boring both to play and to watch. Varying the angle of the racquet and the power behind the shots produces the intricacies and nuances of the game that make it fascinating for player and spectator alike and places the ball precisely where the professional wants it to go.

Many students and beginners freak out when it comes to creating a smile line. Many avoid ever learning how to use white powder, instead choosing the option of using French tips. But the fact is that no one can call him or herself a nail artist if they can't offer clients the 'Permanent French' option on their service menu.

Although a blessing for those who cannot control their white powder, French tips:
- aren't suitable for every nail shape
- don't give as beautiful a result as a perfectly formed, natural-looking smile line made with a variety of different white powders that create different effects and choices. And,
- you can't keep the look permanent for your clients if you can't rebalance and replace the smile as it grows out.

The truth is that at first it's not easy to do a permanent French Manicure using white powder. It's one of the greatest challenges a nail technician faces, but now that you know a bit more about how to use your brush and control what you're doing, it's going to get a lot easier!

Most of the problems encountered when making a smile line are because the angle of the finger isn't correct or the angle of the brush isn't correct or you're stroking with the brush when you should be pressing or pressing when you should be nudging, etc.

Another challenge is using the right pressure on the brush to control exactly where the bead is going. Remember the tennis racquet analogy!

There are many ways to cover Zone 1 and make it smile. I'll describe a couple of different ways in the Product Control chapters and you can try them out for yourself and see which you prefer to adopt.
- working the bead evenly from side to side
- working from the middle out to each side in turn.

The three main brush techniques employed when forming the smile line using liquid and powder are (1 and 2) pressing and patting with the flat side of the brush and (3) nudging with the point or the side of the flattened brush.

Adopting a light touch with the brush is also necessary as is knowing when to apply a firmer pressure.

Remember that your brush is a tool like any other. How you employ it and learning to vary the angle and pressure is paramount if you want to become a professional nail artist, just as mastering all the different shots in a game of tennis produces a champion player.

CHAPTER 6: Brush Control When Using Gels

Using a pre-mixed or gel product for making nail enhancements requires a completely different brush technique than that used for creating liquid/powder enhancements.

The way you use the brush will also be different, as will the angles at which you work with the brush. In fact, the brush is different, being made of synthetic bristles rather than natural hair, which would be too soft to support the product.

As with anything, there are many techniques that can be employed to get a beautiful result with gel. I'll detail a couple of them, but if you're working and making beautiful enhancements using a different technique from those I mention, don't change. If, however, you haven't got a set routine, some of the ideas listed may help you develop your own style and efficient way of working.

Gel products vary, as do the products in other systems. There are many gels that are generic (basically all bought from the same manufacturer and labelled by the supplier) and there are others that are branded and still another with very exciting new technology and patented chemistry. They all have their own 'feel' and characteristics and you as the technician must be adaptable to change and learn how to work differently if you decide to change from one system to another.

Some gels hold their shape, some are runny, some become surface smooth when cured under the UV lamp and others tend to pool or self-level; some are very sticky and stringy and some aren't. Some gels are 'one component' and some are 'three component'. This really means that the system uses one gel for every layer or three different gels to be employed for each different layer.

Whatever type of gel you use, the steps to making an enhancement of one colour are the same: The first layer (generally known as the bonder layer) is thin; the second layer (the builder layer) is thicker, and the final layer (the finishing layer or top coat glossy layer) is thin. Each layer requires a different brush technique.

The Bonder Layer
The grip on the brush is as normal (as described in Brush Control Part 1: Getting A Grip) and the angle of the brush when working is similar to painting a nail.

The bonder layer is always thin and brushed well onto the nail surface. Some describe it as 'scrubbing' the gel onto the surface - but that description always makes me cringe at the thought of the brush doing the scrubbing. Not good for the brush!

I prefer to describe the brushing technique as similar to painting a wall with a brush and emulsion paint. You never paint in one direction only, but in several directions, working the paint smoothly onto the wall. Similarly, this is how you will 'work' the gel onto the nail plate when doing this first bonder layer.

Always make sure that you have control of the brush, and never let the gel touch the skin surrounding the nail plate. If you like you can finish off your brushing in one direction from the eponychium to the free edge, making sure you also carry the gel along the sides and the free edge. Cure under the UV lamp that belongs to your system and for the recommended time for your system.

Make sure as you work, that every layer of gel is brushed onto the sides and free edge of the nail to ensure the entire nail is encased in each layer of gel. This is called 'capping'. If you neglect this step, the gel will tend to split away or chip away from the free edge area later. Remember that gels tend to shrink or pull away from where you have placed them when curing, so you must compensate for this trait by 'capping' the end of the nail.

The Builder Layer

The grip on the brush is as normal and the angle of the brush when working is perpendicular or at a right angle to the nail (handle straight up in the air).

This is the layer where things get very different from liquid/powder technique. The reason for this is that gel is a totally different medium and being sticky, it can't be patted into the shape you want. Instead you must 'tease' it into the shape you want - and very delicately.

Take a scoop of gel onto your brush and then, laying the bristles of the brush across Zone 2, twizzle or twist the brush out of the bead, depositing the bead in Zone 2. The bead should be about the size of a petit pois, or very small pea, for the index, middle and ring fingers; it should be slightly larger for the thumb and smaller for the pinky finger.

Your brush should be in a nice point. Now, holding it with the handle straight up in the air, you'll use only the point of the brush to move parts of the bead where you want them, leaving the bulk of the bead in Zone 2 where you want the apex.

The important thing is not to let the point of the brush come in contact with the nail plate. It should stay on or near the surface of the bead and 'drag' the gel to the area you wish to cover. If you let the brush come in contact with the nail plate, the surface of your enhancement will be lumpy and full of ridges, which will only have to be filed out, or filled in, later.

So let's get back to the bead sitting in Zone 2 waiting to be moved.

I start at the left hand side of the bead (lefties may want to start on the right) and, using the point of my brush, I drag some of the gel from my main bead, up the side of the nail plate to the eponychium and leave it there. I go back to the bead and drag more gel up to the eponychium and so on until Zone 3 is evenly covered.

Next I start again on the left and drag the gel down the left hand side of Zone 1, making sure I cover the edge. I then go back and do the same again, working my way across the tip until it's covered evenly.

The last move is to make sure that the free edge is 'capped', or covered with gel. You can do this simply by brushing gently along the edge of the tip with the gel on your brush.

It's worth having a good look at what you've done from all angles to see if there's anything you need to correct or any 'dips' that need to be filled before curing under the UV lamp.

If you need to fill a gap or a dip, simply touch the point of your brush to the gel on one side of the dip, pick it up and then touch the other side of the dip with the point of the brush. Doing this will pick up a small strand of gel and deposit it where you want it.

You may do this as many times as you need to fill the gap, but be forewarned: the less you 'play' with the gel, the better. Less is definitely more with gel - or things can get more complicated than you want.

When you're satisfied, cure under the UV lamp that belongs to your system and for the recommended time for your system. You may add a second builder layer of gel if needed.

Before buffing to finish, wipe away the sticky inhibition layer of gel with a lint-free pad and the recommended solution for your system.

Using a 180 grit abrasive, gently shape and refine the enhancement. See Chapter 9: Perfect Finishing.

The Top Coat Gloss

The grip on the brush is as normal and the angle of the brush when working is similar to painting a nail.

One of the things that makes gels popular with clients is the permanent nature of the glossy surface of the enhancement. As gels don't break down easily with solvents, the top coat gloss will stay beautifully shiny even after enamel has been removed.

Once all dust has been removed after filing, apply your finishing layer of gel. This layer is pretty much applied as you would apply nail enamel, making sure the sides and free edge are covered.

When satisfied, cure under the UV lamp that belongs to your system and for the recommended time for your system.

Note: It's important to note that there are many different types of gel, and it's always a good thing to do a class with the supplier of your chosen products. It makes sense to let them teach you the techniques that work best for their system. For instance, a different brush technique is used for the builder layer when using the new technology gels from Creative Nail Design. Brisa Gels™ aren't as sticky as generic gels and can be manipulated in a different way.

Important things to remember:
- make sure you 'cap', or cover, the sides and the free edge of the nail enhancement with every layer of gel
- always keep uncured gel off both the client's skin and your own
- there's a tendency to apply gels too thinly. Make sure that your gel enhancements are as strong as a liquid and powder enhancement by giving them the same strength over the stress area.

CHAPTER 7: File Control Part 1 - Getting a Grip

Soon after I started writing for the Nail Geek site I noticed that many people would talk about blending tips as if it were a horrible task they'd take many steps to avoid if possible. But there are times we all need to do it, and the more I thought about it, the more it seemed people tried to avoid it because they found it hard to do and/or it was taking too much time.

Not only is blending in a tip without causing any nail damage a skill that all can learn - it needn't take a lot of time to do, either. If tip blending is time-consuming for you, there can be only one or two reasons:
1. you're using tips that are difficult to blend (some are very easy), or,
2. you're not filing efficiently.

Buying good quality tips is the easy bit. The harder part is changing how you hold your abrasive.

Using your abrasive efficiently will take a change of grip, and perseverance until the new process feels comfortable (it will feel weird for a few days until you've mastered it). A teacher of mine (bless her) passed a tip on to me many years ago that I in turn have passed on to many others. Now I'll share it with you.

Most nail technicians don't hold their abrasives correctly for the job they want to do.

They hold the abrasive with their thumb on the top and fingers underneath and file that way for most jobs. We all tend to change the grip for doing the sidewalls and shaping.

But 90% of the jobs we do are done with the grip described above.

When I want to do a job and get it over with as quickly as possible (like blending tips and removing product) with the minimum amount of effort and the maximum amount of efficiency, I hold it this way:

- Grab hold of the abrasive as if you were shaking hands with it. Then extend only your index finger out and onto the abrasive. Then, lifting your elbow and placing the abrasive onto the product (still holding it the same way), start to do your work with your finger over the area you're filing. This way the maximum pressure is under your finger where you want it to be, and this in turn removes the product faster. It also gives you more control and reduces the chance of causing a burning sensation because there's no air trapped under the abrasive.

Remember what we learned in the Girl Guides: Air + Friction = Fire = Ouch!

Holding the abrasive in the old way with thumb on the top gives too light a pressure which takes too long, gives you less control so that it's easier to damage the natural nail, traps air between the abrasive and the product (which in turn causes a heat sensation) and creates pressure that kinks, bends and eventually breaks your abrasives.

These are excellent reasons for learning to hold your abrasive in a different way for those times when there is a 'job of work' to be done.

CHAPTER 8: File Control Part 2

Now that you've got a grip on the new filing technique, we'll move on to the method of actually thinning and blending a tip so the job is made as quick and easy as possible with no nail plate damage.

First of all, why do we blend and thin tips anyway? Clearly some technicians just cut out the well of the tip, adhere it to the plate and apply product to it. So why do the work if it isn't needed?

Well, the work is needed for several reasons:
>   1. sometimes for the sake of beauty, it's necessary to blend a tip.
>   2. it's always necessary to thin out a tip for the sake of strength.

Those who don't do this will have clients with more breakages than those who do.

Those who don't do this will have free edges that look wide and bulky - also known as 'Egyptian Hats' (a phrase coined by Creative Nail Design's Jan Arnold many moons ago).

Any technician who uses tips (whether all the time or only when feeling that sculpting isn't an option) should be trying to get as close to a sculpted nail as possible. To do this, it's necessary to blend away the tip well area (for clarity) and to thin the rest of the tip (for strength).

The product is always stronger than a tip. This means thinning out the tip is important so the most product can go on top of the tip and still have it look thin and beautiful. In other words, you're only using your tip as a foundation or 'canvas' for the product to cling to.

The following is the most efficient method for thinning and blending a tip, using the grip taught in Part 1. I use a 180 x 240 abrasive for this job.

Most technicians start to blend a tip at the well area! Here's a better idea: it's more efficient to start thinning the tip at the free edge and then move back toward the well area, which is blended last.

Why? Because it's the safest way to ensure that absolutely no nail plate damage is caused. Plus, it's quicker. Anything safe that makes filing quicker is worth doing as filing is so boring!

Think it through. If you start to thin at the free edge, you're going to progressively thin the tip and eventually the well area as you move toward it.

By the time you get to the well area, you will already have gone a long way toward getting the work done in that area, as the abrasive moves up and down while you work. The good thing is you won't even have touched the natural nail plate during the process and most of the work will be done.

Once you've actually reached the well area, slow down, switch to the smooth side of the abrasive and, during the last few moments (while you blend the last bit away), make sure your abrasive stays on the well area of the tip and doesn't touch the plate.

Using this technique is quick, efficient, and takes only a little thought and a responsible attitude toward the health of your clients' natural nails to do a good, safe job.

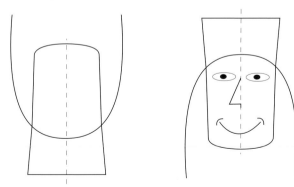

Jan's 'Egyptian Hat' nail

CHAPTER 9: File Control Part 3 - Perfect Finishing

Have you ever noticed on some of the advertisements in the nail magazines that the nails are (shall we say?) far from perfect examples of a beautifully finished nail enhancement?

How can you tell? Usually, the light shining on the nails looks all wobbly or patchy, which shows all the flaws on the surface. Or the outline of the nail (what I call the form) is not pleasing to the eye. Or the shape (the view from the side) has apexes all over the place!

On the other hand, we all remember those images in advertisements of beautiful, sleek, gorgeous, shiny nail enhancements done by (shall we say?) technicians who really know what they are doing.

How can you tell? The light shining on the nail surface in the image is consistent in width and straight as an arrow and there are no flaws on the surface to mar its beauty. The form is perfect (beautiful straight sidewalls) and the shape is a natural and gentle curve with the apex in the right place.

If you aren't sure you're getting a perfect finish to your nail enhancements, use this valuable tool to help you in achieving the ultimate flawless result you want. We call it 'the line of light'.

But first, before you use the line of light to guide you, before you look, you need to finish off the enhancement nearly all the way. Your finishing will be easier still if you stick to the rule of trying to make the perfect nail with your brush rather than relying on your file to do it for you. This is best all around: better for the life of the enhancement, better for the natural nail, and better for you because, as we've said before, filing is boring for both you and your clients.

For the purpose of this chapter, we're going to assume that you have not made the perfect nail with your brush, so I can go through all the steps of perfect finishing and explain what each step achieves.

So we're looking at the unfinished nail enhancement. And we're going to make a soft square shape.

The first thing I correct is the form (the outline). Using a medium-soft abrasive (I use a 240 grit), make sure your sidewalls are absolutely straight, with no bulges at the waist and no free edges that look wide and unattractive.

File gently up and down each side of the nail, keeping the abrasive trapped gently by your thumb on one side or by your index finger on the other to make sure it doesn't deviate from the straight line at all. It's a common fault for right-handed people to pull the abrasive across to the right when doing the left side of the nail (the opposite for lefties); this tends to round off one side of the enhancement while the other stays nice and straight.

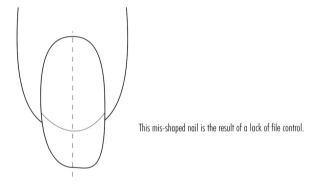

This mis-shaped nail is the result of a lack of file control.

Be careful! Once you've done it, this is difficult to correct without making the nail shorter, which won't please a client who wants long nails.

Next, shape the free edge into a gentle curve and, from underneath, just angle the abrasive to remove any harsh corners.

My next move is to lay the abrasive flat onto Zone 3 of the nail and gently blend any excess product into the nail so it's impossible to see where the enhancement actually joins the natural nail. This job done, you won't need to go to Zone 3 or the sidewalls again and can concentrate on the business of making that shape perfect. Plus, there will be no need to go near any soft tissue because the fiddly bits are done.

Now we come to the three paths to success! Looking at the whole enhancement held with my fingers, I mentally divide the nail into three vertical paths, one down the middle and one down each side.

The perfect shape is achieved by looking at the side view of the nail first and seeing where, if any, corrections need to be made with the abrasive to make the side view perfect. Don't worry about the side paths yet, just concentrate on the curvature of the nail. Then, using the same medium-soft abrasive and working in an east to west direction, start at the north end of the nail and work south, putting more pressure on the abrasive where you want to remove any undesirable lumps or bumps. Keep going up and down until when you look from the side, you see that the curvature is how you want it to be. The shape or curve that you create here I call the 'design line' and after you have created it everything else you do will work up to this 'design line'.

Next move is to go to each side in turn and, working from the side to the middle in one direction, bring the sides up to your 'design line' and the curve you have created there.

You must work with your abrasive in a nice curvy motion as if you were filing the surface of an egg. This will give your enhancement a really natural C curve.

Now for the line of light! Apply some cuticle oil and rub it into the surface of the enhancement. Then check under your light and see what the line of light is telling you, as you slowly rotate the finger to see the light play over the surface.

You should be looking for a even width all the way along the light line:
- if it widens, you have a flat spot
- if it narrows, you have a facet
- if it wiggles, you have a dip or a high spot.

Make any necessary adjustments with your abrasive and check again.

Finally, finish off to a high-gloss shine. Your soft buffers won't change the surface other than to make it gleam and reflect your fine workmanship.

CHAPTER 10: File Control Part 4 - The Rebalance

The rebalance is the procedure most often carried out by nail technicians, and many new technicians are surprised at just how long this process takes. The rebalance actually is a relatively quick process if there are no problems to correct, but enhancements are not indestructible and inevitably problems such as breakages and lifting can occur during the time between appointments. However, these things should not be the norm but the exception.

For instance, you shouldn't have to thin the cuticle area during a rebalance other than to tidy it up and check that all the edges are sealed, as it should already be so thin you can't tell where it joins the new growth of the natural nail. You shouldn't have to thin out or remove half the product on the enhancement before re-applying - only in the areas you need to adjust.

Normally, the rebalance should be about assessing the nails and then maintaining them with an eye to preventing future problems rather than correcting present ones.

This chapter will emphasise a different method of using your abrasive to get the job done quickly and efficiently.

Many technicians do far more filing during the rebalance than is necessary. And we all know that filing for long periods of time when there is no need is boring for everyone.

Lots of filing also creates lots of dust and can cause unnecessary trauma both to the product and the natural nail. So let's avoid it when we can.

Always use a good sharp new abrasive for the rebalance, as it will make the job much faster and easier. I use one with a 180x240 grit.

One thing you must consider is whether or not there is more lift on your clients' nails than there should be. It is common for amateurs to get lifting at the sides and the cuticle area because they go too near, or touch the skin with the product. Sometimes the lift is caused by product being applied too thickly. Remember to keep a small margin around the nail plate free of product when you apply. Work with less product and lifting will become a thing of the past, or at least a rarity.

If you do see lifting, don't be one of the many technicians that spend much energy and time 'chasing the line' of lifted material down the nail plate, filing and filing until half the product has been removed. There is no need.

Do you know why you're chasing the line down the nail? Because you're filing on top of the area that's already lifted instead of filing on the part of the enhancement that's still adhered firmly to the nail! This creates unsightly and unsanitary 'fill lines' which remain visible on the completed nail.

When you file on top of the lifted product, which is already loose, you just shake loose everything below where you're filing and end up chasing the line until you reach an area where the product is thicker and so therefore won't shake loose so easily. What a waste of time and effort! What a chore! If you concentrate instead on filing just below the lifted area (where the product is firmly attached), you won't loosen anything further and when you 'break through' to the natural nail, the lifted bit will just pop off and there will be no fill lines and no nail damage, either. Take this little gem of information and use it - and your life as a nail technician will be changed forever.

When faced with a rebalance, a technician tends to look at the nails then head straight for the problem area on each one - i.e., the lift if there is any. And, yes, if that's what you do, then removing the lifted material by filing through the product immediately would be time-consuming. But if you tackle the rebalance Zone by Zone - in the same way you'd apply the product or thin and blend a tip, then the whole job is quicker and more efficient.

Change your mind set, dare to think in a different way, and, 'hey, presto' the job's easy!

Start the rebalance procedure at Zone 1 (the tip). Shorten it, thin it and re-shape it.

Then move on to Zone 2 (the stress area), thinning it slightly and checking carefully for any cracks, bare spots or weak spots. If all is well, move on to Zone 3.

When you get to Zone 3 (the cuticle area, which is already the thinnest zone anyway, and where you're most likely to find lifting), you'll already have been thinning it as your abrasive has moved up and down during the process of preparing Zones 1 and 2, so the product will already be partially thinned when you start to work in this area.

Use the 180 side to do the bulk of the work, switching to the 240 side as you get nearer to the natural nail, and the last bit of lifted material will flake away. Carefully and gently blend any ledge of product seamlessly into the nail plate. Remember to keep the abrasive moving firmly and evenly so as not to cause any fires!

After you've re-applied your new product, your re-balanced nails will look like a brand-new set.

personal notes

CHAPTER 11: Product Control Part 1
Mix Ratio

If you want to have perfect control with your brush, it does go hand in hand that you must also have perfect control of your product. Despite claims to the contrary by some companies, it is essential to mix your product correctly, and there is no such thing as a product that works and lasts perfectly, no matter what ratio of liquid to powder you use!

It would be nice, but it's not real life.

Obviously there is an 'ideal' mix (which varies with different products); however, it's not the end of the world, and you won't encounter big problems, if your mix varies either toward slightly too wet or slightly too dry. The problems come when one goes farther to either side of the perfect mixture. Not only will there be problems with the enhancements you produce, but your brush won't be able to control the bead, which will make your life as a nail technician much more difficult than it needs to be. Learn to make the correct mix always. Here's how!

There are so many ways to achieve the correct mix, and they're all right, if, at the end of the day, you've got it right!

Brushes vary as to how much liquid they hold and people vary as to how long they leave the brush in the powder, etc., but even taking these variables into consideration, it is possible for every technician to get the perfect mix ratio every time.

To help you, I 'll tell you my method and you can give it a try. Whatever brush you use, it's important to know how much liquid it holds.

Now, let's make a medium-sized bead. First (when starting with a dry brush), gently flatten out your brush in the bottom of the dappen dish of monomer, to release all the air trapped in the brush. Fully load your brush with liquid. Now, draw your brush gently but firmly out against the side of the dappen dish (and not just the tip of the brush - draw down the entire length of the hairs of the brush from the shaft to flags). This will flatten the brush and release some of the liquid. Do this first on one side of the brush and then the other. Use medium pressure (the hairs of the brush shouldn't bend), and watch the side of the dappen dish to see how much you have squeezed out. It's surprising how much liquid is released from the brush.

Next, balance your wrist on the table near the dappen dish and, holding your brush so that the handle is straight up in the air, draw a line in your powder, with only the flags of the brush, about 5-6mm long (1/4 of an inch).

Lift the brush out of the powder and then watch the bead absorb the powder. It should take about two seconds or the time it takes you to say, 'one, two, three!'. If the powder has absorbed straight away and has a slick, shiny appearance before you can finish saying, 'one, two, three!' then the bead is too wet. If there is still powder on the top of the bead that is not being absorbed, then it's too dry.

If too wet, try again - doing everything exactly the same but remembering to either keep your brush in the powder a little longer, by drawing your line a little longer, or to squeeze a bit more liquid out of your brush before drawing your line the same length as before.

One thing or the other has to be changed to alter the mix ratio of the bead.

If too dry, start again and remember to draw your line a little shorter this time.

Never wipe your brush prior to dipping it into the powder in order to eliminate liquid from it. This is a costly waste of liquid, and it creates much more vapour in the air, and therefore more smell, as well as an over-exposure hazard.

The telltale sign of an incorrect mix is the product being a bit difficult to handle once you start to work it on the nail (either difficult to control or difficult to press out). Your bead should be easy to handle and control and there should be no product residue left on the brush when you finish working the bead.

Once you've found the method that works for you, do it every time. You'll need to have a method for small, medium and large beads. Usually this is only a matter of releasing a bit more liquid from the brush when you want to size down.

Once you've created a bead that has the look of wet sugar or wet snow, press the bead onto the nail, then take a breath (again like counting to three), before starting to work the bead. In other words, give the polymerisation process a chance to get going for a second or two before you start to press out the bead. By relaxing a little and letting the process start, you'll eliminate the chance of developing bubbles in your product.

You'll know to start working the bead when it changes and looks nice and shiny and wet on the nail.

Below is a diagram to show the different angles of the brush handle when making the different Zones.

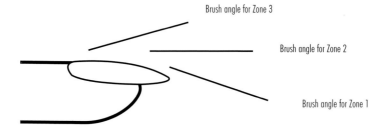

Brush angle for Zone 3

Brush angle for Zone 2

Brush angle for Zone 1

CHAPTER 12: Product Control Part 2
Zone 1 - Making it Smile!

Once a bead of product is placed onto the nail, the first time you press, it immediately moves or 'squishes' the bead into a different position. So if you place your bead directly onto the smile line, the first press will immediately push it above the smile line, giving the nail bed a shortened appearance. So place the bead onto the nail just below the smile line because when you position it there, the first press will move up to the smile line where you want it to be. This puts you in control instead of the bead being in control of you.

OK. With that sorted, there's another thing you need to know: the quicker you accomplish making the smile line, the easier it will be. Don't worry at first about covering all of the tip - just get that smile line created and worry about the rest of the tip afterwards. If you need to add more product because your bead was to small, then it's always easier to add it to the tip than to the smile line. As you get more competent at judging the correct size of the bead and work faster, you will do it all in one go.

You can work your smile line in a variety of ways. Below are two of them. Remember to keep your brush angled so that the thickest part of the white is only at the smile line, getting thinner toward the free edge. This means you either have to raise the finger a little or lower the handle of your brush. Do one thing or the other to get the right angle.

The most common fault of beginners and students is that they use the point of the brush to stab or prod the product into place when creating the smile line, which gives an uneven surface both in texture and in colour.

Remember to lay the flat of your brush onto the bead and gently press and push a little at a time. This goes for both methods below. A light touch is the key.

Working the bead evenly from side to side
Place your medium-sized bead of white powder in the centre of the smile line and just below it. Still using the flat side of the brush at the correct angle, lightly make baby presses and push the bead first up and to the right (just a little) and then up and to the left (just a little), then back to the right and then the left, working from side to side in turn, keeping the bead soft and pliable and always nudging it a little farther up and into the corners as you go from side to side.

Eventually, go up into each corner, using the edge or side of the flattened brush, which effectively gives you a point to work with. You need to use the point in the corners so you don't touch the skin with the wet brush.

Once you get your corners in place, you can gently smooth the product from the smile line over the rest of the tip, keeping your brush at the appropriate angle. Remember to do this gently, or you can spoil the nice line you've made. If you don't have enough product to cover the tip, just add more at the tip and smooth. With practice, you'll learn to gauge the right amount.

Working from the middle out to each side in turn.
Another way to make your white powder smile is to place your medium-sized bead of white powder in the centre of the smile line and just below it. Still using the flat side of the brush at the correct angle, lightly make baby presses and push the bead first up and to the right (just a little at a time) until you go right up into the right corner. Then do the same on the left side.

Once you get your corners in place, you can gently smooth the product from the smile line over the rest of the tip, keeping your brush at the appropriate angle. Remember to do this gently or you can spoil the nice line you've made.

Most right-handed people tend to complete the right corner first and then the left - the opposite for 'lefties'. It's strange, but many technicians have found they do better smiles when they reverse this habit and start to make the smile line on the opposite side to the one that they're used to. I can't explain why this might be, but it works for me.

I also find that I need to work quickly when doing the smile line in this way or else the product is apt to become too set on one side and it's difficult to smooth out over the rest of the tip.

CHAPTER 13: Product Control Part 3
Zone 2 - Making it Last!

The most common fault of beginners and students is that they use the brush at the wrong angle when creating the 'stress' area, which gives a bulky and barrel-like appearance to the finished enhancement. Remember, the brush angle in Zone 2 should be almost parallel to the nail.

The thickest part of the enhancement is Zone 2 (also known as the stress area and the apex), where the nail takes the pressure when put under stress. Although this is the thickest part of the enhancement, it shouldn't be 'thick', but just a touch thicker than the product at the smile line.

This Zone should never cover more than half the visible nail plate. This is important, as you must leave enough room in Zone 3 to work the bead without touching the skin in that Zone.

It's also important that you leave no 'ledge' of product in Zone 2. The product should 'melt' into the nail plate.

This will ensure that you don't end up with 2 apexes (or ridges) in the enhancement that you have to file away later. In order to achieve this melting into the nail effect, you must learn to push and then pull the bead in one easy, fluid movement of the brush.

It's very important that when you lay your brush on the bead, the flags of the brush extend just a tiny bit over the edge of the bead and aren't resting in the middle of it. If the flags aren't in the correct position, you'll force up another ledge of product, which you definitely do not want.

The push/pull method is similar to the movement you use when applying nail enamel.

When you've placed your liquid/powder bead in the position you want then let it settle for a second or two, lay your brush on the bead and push it toward the eponychium (gently but firmly) first (just enough to thin out the 'ledge' of product), before pulling your brush (lightly) over the rest of the enhancement to the tip. You will also employ this method for Zone 3. Learn to vary your pressure for the push (firm but gentle) and the pull (light).

At first, many technicians fear that pushing the bead will back the product into the brush and make it gooey. If your mix is correct, this won't happen, so just go for it and try the method because it will change both your life as a technician and the look and durability of your enhancements. This method will also reduce filing, because the enhancements will be beautiful and well-balanced before you start to file them. Less filing means stronger enhancements, less dust and less work for you. You win all the way around when you incorporate this method of application.

Zone 2 Application

Press the correct-sized bead firmly just above the smile line and immediately draw your brush lightly all the way down over the tip. Let the bead relax for a second or two.

Press one side of the bead out until it almost, but doesn't quite, touch the side and as soon as you get there, immediately push and pull and smooth the bead into the smile line by drawing your brush lightly all the way down over the tip.

Go back to push and pull and smooth again between the stroke you've just done and the centre of the nail and draw your brush lightly all the way down over the tip. Stop there.

Now press the other side of the bead out until it almost but doesn't quite touch the other side, and, as soon as you get there, immediately push and pull and smooth the bead into the smile line by drawing your brush lightly all the way down over the tip.

Go back and push and pull and smooth again just between the stroke you've just done and the centre of the nail and draw your brush lightly all the way down over the tip. Stop in the centre of the nail.

Can you see how using this method builds up the product in the centre of the nail and leaves it thin at the sides and the junction of Zone 3? This is what your main objective should be. This method produces balance, which will keep the enhancements strong. Your last stroke should always end at the middle of the nail.

CHAPTER 14: Product Control Part 4
Zone 3 - Making it Disappear

In this area, too, the most common fault of beginners and students is using the brush at the wrong angle (see brush control) when trying to make the product 'meld' with the nail, which in turn scoops the product from Zone 3 into Zone 2, making Zone 2 look bulky and Zone 3 too thin or uneven.

Keep the brush handle only slightly raised, the merest bit higher than it was in Zone 2. The finished Zone 3 should be thin but even and should 'melt' into the natural nail so it isn't possible to tell where the enhancement ends and the natural nail begins.

The second most common fault is placing the bead into the small gap that is left showing in Zone 3. This is the wrong placement of the bead and is the principal cause of product touching the skin, which will always cause lifting. Placing the bead in the gap leaves you with no room to work. The restriction on your space means that as soon as you start to work the bead, it touches the skin.

You must have control of the bead at this stage of your work, and placement of the bead is very important.

Using the push and pull method in this Zone also ensures no lifting and a thin and even coverage of Zone 3.

The push action firmly presses the product onto the nail surface (hence, no lifting) and the pull smoothes out and distributes the product evenly.

Make the correct-sized bead and place it in the centre of the nail and on the tapered edge of the completed Zone 2.

Gently but firmly press the flat side of the brush onto the bead and push the product up to, but not touching, the centre of the eponychium; then, in one fluid movement, draw your brush lightly all the way down over the tip. Go back and do the same at each side, pushing the product back firmly and then smoothing forward lightly all the way down and over the tip.

Following through all the way over the tip with your brush strokes when you do each Zone ensures a silky-smooth finish, as all the Zones are drawn together. The silkier and smoother the finish, the less filing there is to do later.

Creating the different pressures is very important. You want firm pressure so the product makes good contact with the dry nail surface, but then you want light pressure so you don't move or scoop the product into a Zone where you don't want it. The smoother the surface, the easier finishing will be.

I always finish with a few extra strokes from one side to the centre and then the other side to the centre, making sure the bulk of the product is always in the middle of the nail.

It's common to see nails that have a nice form but look 'flat' and uninteresting.

This is due to lack of brush technique. Good brush technique lets you build the product up in the centre of the nail so it has a lovely 'C' curve all along its length.

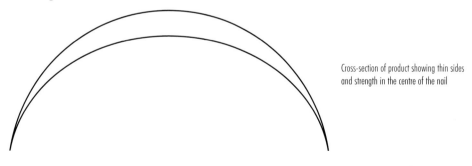

Cross-section of product showing thin sides and strength in the centre of the nail

CHAPTER 15: The Forever French Rebalance

Working with Pink and White powder to produce a beautiful set of French enhancements does create the challenge for the nail technician to keep them looking like a new set, month after month after month.

Inevitably the white portion of the enhancement moves with the growth of the natural nail and would ultimately disappear altogether if not replaced on a regular basis.

Clients love to perpetuate the French look, they become addicted to it, so in order to provide them with the Forever French service, you need to know how to do it in a timely and efficient manner.

Most technicians find that the biggest obstacle to providing the Forever French service is the large amount of preparation and filing they think they have to do in order to prepare the enhancements for this service. Actually, it really needn't take much more time than an ordinary maintenance appointment if you follow the guidelines in this chapter.

Many think, or have been taught, that they must file away vast amounts of product only to replace it again with new product! Why? There is no need to do this at all. There's no need to use an electric file to carve a 'ditch' or 'trough' in the product to remove the white either. If you do this then the smile line never looks perfect again and, in my opinion, the finished nails look 'patched up'.

Think clearly about what you have to do:
- You need to thin the enhancement in the area where you renew the smile line with white. (Zone 1)
- You need to replace the apex of the product in the correct new location (because of course it has moved out of position along with the re-growth of the natural nail, just as the smile line has). (Zone 2)
- You need to prepare and replace Zone 3 as normal.

There's no need to thin the product any more than you absolutely have to in order to achieve these three objectives.

Preparing the Enhancements

Two things are most important to remember:

- Only remove product where you need to and
- Only replace with the amount of product you need (which should equal the amount you removed) for the finished 'look'. This means that your beads of product will only be tiny compared to the size of bead that you make when doing a new full set.

Assuming that the original set was done using White and Pink powder (not only a white French tip) use the following method.

Shorten and restore the enhancement length to the original length of the full set. Once you have done this, you will see that the new free edge is now thicker than it was before. You will need to thin it out to the finished thickness that you want... no more.

Next, holding your abrasive and using the grip described in File Control - Part 1, thin out the enhancement with the pressure concentrated over the area where the natural nail smile line can be seen and just above it, where the apex is situated. You only need to reduce the thickness of the product in this area by half... no more.

Make sure that the product remaining in the former Zone 3 area it tight and flush to the natural nail.

Applying the Product
Remember that there's still white product in Zone 1. All you need to do is to add a beautiful new smile line.

When applying the new smile line... this only requires a very small amount of product (it is going to sit on top of old product, so work with a much smaller bead here so that the nail does not look chunky when you come to add the zone 2 bead), then just smooth the new product into the existing old white product.

You're not trying to cover the whole of Zone 1 again; there's no need, because most of it's still white. Of course you must do your usual check to make sure the sides of Zone 1 are firmly 'clamped' to the natural nail that is growing out underneath. This will ensure no curling away of the natural nail from the tip area. Make sure you do not file away the 'clamp' when finishing off.

Next, replace Zone 2 with a very small bead; this small bead should fill the gap between the smile line and the new location of the apex for both strength and beauty.

It is important not to oversize this bead or the enhancement will look too bulbous in Zone 2. Don't forget to replace the product at the sidewalls where the nail is bare.

Finally, fill in Zone 3 as normal with a small bead of product and draw the bead into and over as much of Zone 2 as you need to in order to keep the apex in the correct position.

The most common fault on the part of technicians when doing a French Rebalance is using way too much new product. The result is a bulky looking nail instead of the sleek look you hopefully had in the original full set. This bulky look causes you to file and file to remove excess product and usually the new smile line gets removed along with it and you're back to 'square one'.

Removing the correct amount of product during preparation and replacing it with the right amount of new product will ensure this doesn't happen to you.

The French Rebalance is actually an enjoyable service to perform for your clients, and they are always impressed with the fact that the whole set of enhancements looks brand spanking new, fresh and beautiful.

CHAPTER 16: What on Earth is a Lower Arch?

You might well ask this question because the lower arch is something that is ignored by most teachers when it comes to nail design, yet it's a touch of finesse that, when incorporated into your work, adds undeniable class and beauty that sets it apart from all the rest.

So what and where is it exactly? Do we need it? How do we incorporate it?

Visualise how a nail would look from the side view if it were allowed to grow and grow and grow. We've all seen pictures of ultra-long nails, and it isn't difficult to visualise how they curve and curl when allowed to grow indefinitely. I've never seen a natural nail that, when very long, grows out in a straight line from the free edge. With the exception of the misshapen nail, as in the case of a ski-jump nail growing in an upward curve, the natural line in which a nail grows is that of a gentle curve from the free edge downwards. This is the lower arch.

The shorter the nail plate, the more difficult it is to see the lower arch, but give it some length and the arch is more pronounced. So to find it, look from the side view, at the sidewall from the point where the nail plate leaves the nail bed (the free edge).

It's essential, in my view, to be conscious of the need to incorporate the lower arch into the nail enhancement, and the longer the nail, the more it needs to be incorporated. If no account is taken of the lower arch as another natural dimension of the nail enhancement, then the design of the enhancement looks false and unnatural. Every nail has a natural upper arch, which we as technicians recognise and go to great lengths to make look natural and graceful. If that upper arch is not complimented by a corresponding lower arch, the look is unbalanced and unattractive.

There are four main ways to incorporate the lower arch into your work as a nail technician.

The first is to use tips that already have the lower arch built into the design of the tip.

There are many tips that do not have a marked lower arch, and if you use them, the second way is to create the lower arch yourself. Do this simply by using a pair of curved scissors and cutting a very gentle curve into the sidewall of the tip starting from the 'stop point' of the contact area and cutting toward the end of the free edge of the tip. You don't have to cut all the way down the length of the tip - only as far as the length you're making the finished nail. Need I say that you need to do this prior to adhering the tip to the natural nail?

The third way to fashion the lower arch is to add it to your free-form sculpted design in Zone 1. When sculpting this Zone, make sure that while keeping the sidewalls parallel, you also carve the lower arch into the sidewall with the tip of your brush. Just nudge the sidewall into a gentle curve with the point of your brush, and there you have it!

The fourth method is to use a padded abrasive to file the lower arch into the tip.

However, this method takes a lot of practice, and using curved scissors is much easier.

Again, if you use an abrasive, it needs to be done prior to adhering the tip to the natural nail.

The effect of creating the lower arch, be it on a tip or when free-form sculpting, is twofold. One, it adds grace and beauty to your design, and, two, it makes the free edge a little more narrow and sleek. Creating a lower arch is also the way to make bitten nails look less wide and white tips more narrow.

CHAPTER 17: Perfect Form - It's all a Matter of Degree

No matter how well you've prepared your nails, no matter how perfect your mix ratio, no matter how brilliantly you control your product and your brush, in the end, it's the final look of the enhancements that matters to your client. If the final look doesn't please, then the technician is in for trouble.

The final look is all about consistency. Creating the exact same form on every nail is of paramount importance and, as usual, in order to achieve this, you must adopt a 'system' or technique and stick to it rigidly for each nail.

Let's define the terms first so we know what we are talking about.

Most people refer to the shape of the nail as being almond, round, square, square round (or soft square), squoval (or tapered square), stiletto, etc. But these terms don't really apply to the shape - they apply to the form, to the outline of the nail. This is the view we see when looking straight onto the top of the finger. This view is one - dimensional.

Shape refers to the side view of the nail, which is three-dimensional, having depth and height and length. This chapter is concerned with creating the perfect **form** time after time after time.

It's not possible for you to draw the form you want to make onto the nail itself. Instead, you must develop an eye for perfect form and be able to see it in your mind. Looking at beautiful images of perfect nails is a good way to develop your eye, and it will help you create your own perfection. As always, though, there are some simple rules that will help you create the final picture.

Learn to visualise an invisible centre line that runs down the nail.

Know that to create symmetry, the sidewalls must be exactly the same length on each side of the nail and on every nail.

Know that to create symmetry, the angle from the centre line to the sidewalls must be the same from each side of the centre line to the sidewalls and the same on every nail.

Once you learn and stick to these 3 simple rules, the rest is easy. It's all a matter of degree!

The Perfect Square Nail (or Competition Nail)

- make sure the sidewalls are of equal length, perfectly straight and parallel to each other
- at the free edge, the angle from both sides of the centre line to the sidewalls should be 90°.

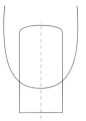

The Soft Square Nail (or Rounded Square)

- make sure the sidewalls are of equal length, perfectly straight and parallel to each other
- at the free edge, the arc from both sides of the centre line to the sidewalls should be very gently curved and not straight across
- use your abrasive from the underside of the nail and gently soften or 'round' (using no pressure) each corner off with a gentle rocking motion.

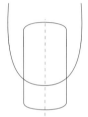

The Tapered Square Nail (or Squoval)

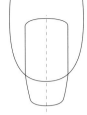

- make sure the sidewalls are of equal length, perfectly straight but tapered in slightly (at the same angle on each side) toward the centre line
- at the free edge, the arc from both sides of the centre line to the sidewalls should be very gently curved and not straight across
- use your abrasive from the underside of the nail and gently soften or round (using no pressure) each corner off with a gentle rocking motion.

The Round Nail

- make sure the sidewalls are of equal length, perfectly straight but tapered in slightly (at the same angle on each side) toward the centre line
- at the free edge, the arc from both sides of the centre line to the sidewalls should be more dramatically curved until a rounded appearance is achieved. Always use the abrasive from the underside of the enhancement, so you can see what you are doing. Work from the centre line to the sidewalls on each side and make sure the arc of the curve is the same from both sides of the centre line to the sidewalls
- there will be no corners on this nail.

The Almond Nail

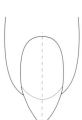

- make sure the sidewalls are of equal length (short, in this case), perfectly straight but tapered in slightly (at the same angle on each side) toward the centre line
- the angle of the arc from the centre line to the sidewalls should be 45°
- the centre point and all other angles should be gently softened from the underside of the nail using a rocking motion with the abrasive. Nothing should look sharp.

The Stiletto Nail

- make sure the sidewalls are of equal length (short, in this case), perfectly straight but tapered in slightly (at the same angle on each side) toward the centre line
- the angle from the centre line to the sidewalls should be 30°-35° and can be cut into the tip, before product application, using a pair of curved scissors to save time filing
- the point and all other angles should be gently softened from the underside of the nail using a rocking motion with the abrasive. This nail will look very dramatic and stylised.

The Asymmetrical Lipstick Nail

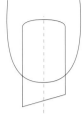

- in the case of this nail form, the sidewalls are of unequal length but should be the same for every nail. It's up to the technician and client to determine the appropriate length for the client
- the angle from the centre line to each sidewall will comply with joining up the asymmetrical walls by using the abrasive at the appropriate angle
- the corners can be softened or not as the technician and the client see fit.

I hope you now see how each nail form is changed only by the degree of the angle or arc from the centre line to the sidewalls and the length and angle of the sidewalls.

Developing an eye for seeing the form you want to achieve is as important as the system you use to create it.

Developing a system that works for you is the key to decreasing your time with each client. Clients expect a professional to take a certain acceptable amount of time for each appointment. The time taken should allow the client to relax and to feel pampered, too.

CHAPTER 18: Precision Polishing

Most of we girls take it for granted that we know how to polish nails - after all, we've been doing it since we were about 12 years old, right? Why is it then that you can tell a professional polish job from the do-it-yourself variety from a mile away? What makes the professional precision polish different?

- it's glossy and shiny
- it's much longer lasting
- there are no brush marks, streaks or snags
- the perimeter lines are perfect and there's no polish on the skin.

All the attributes of a professional precision polish are achieved by using certain techniques that the average woman doesn't know about.

Let's start at the beginning by using a top-quality enamel that has a beautiful brush (very important), gives excellent coverage, never goes thick in the bottle, dries quickly, and is a professional brand of the highest quality and not one that your clients can buy in the drugstore. These are things every professional should demand from the polish line she uses.

It's always necessary to loosen up the polish by rolling the bottle between the palms of your hands. Is this just an affectation? Can't you just shake it up? In a word, no. If you shake a bottle of polish, it will be full of thousands of bubbles that can come to the top and create little craters in the surface of your polish later. So 'roll' the bottle of your chosen polish in the palms of your hands the professional way.

Believe it or not, most amateurs don't even load the brush or remove it from the bottle correctly. This results in tops that won't come off the bottle unless you run them under very hot water to loosen them and sticky, gunked-up caps. No one has time in the salon to deal with these problems, so it's best to develop the correct methods in the first place.

To begin, take the little finger of the client's right hand and hold it with the thumb, index and middle finger of your non-dominant hand (just as you would when applying product - see Brush Control Part 1). Hold the bottle in the palm of your hand, keeping it secure with your ring and pinky fingers.

Next, loosen the cap on the polish bottle and hold it as described in Brush Control Part 1. Pull the brush out of the bottle away from you, and remove the polish from the far side of the brush. Using this technique leaves the brush in the perfect position to get started, with the polish on the correct side of the brush for you to work efficiently and no sticky bottle necks.

Always start with a base coat on a nail that is completely free of oil and contamination. Choose a base coat designed to be soft and to attract the polish to it smoothly. A base coat shouldn't be formulated to be hard and protective - that's the job of the top coat.

Making sure your polishing hand is balanced correctly, place the loaded brush in the middle of the nail and apply gentle pressure on the brush to fan it out and spread the bristles, which (if it's a good brush) should be gently curved in the shape of the eponychium. Once fanned out, push back, up to but not touching the eponychium, and then pull quickly toward you with light pressure to the free edge. The amount of top coat on the brush now will be less and you can use it to fill in either side of the unfinished nail without fear of the polish running into the nail grooves.

Finally, take the side of the brush and run it along the free edge so it also gets a coat.

If your brush runs out, always finish in a straight line so when you come back with a newly loaded brush, it will meld together seamlessly with the coat on the nail.

Next, add the chosen colour immediately. Apply this coat slowly and methodically but in exactly the same way (the 'push/pull' method), making sure you don't drag the bristles along the nail, instead using very light strokes, which will create a smooth surface.

Don't forget to run the side of the brush along the edge of the free edge, and be sure to leave a tiny free margin at the sidewalls and the eponychium.

Colour adds illusion to your nail design. Nails look sleeker and slimmer when you leave a free margin around the nail plate. You can rotate the finger to make sure you get as close as possible without touching the soft tissue surrounding the plate. Use your thumb and index finger to 'pinch' the skin away from the plate to give you more room to work.

The second coat of colour will always go on quickly as you've already established your edges and can more easily follow what you have done before. Keep your strokes very light and quick for perfect smoothness, almost flicking the brush over the surface.

Last, apply your chosen topcoat in the same method and with very light strokes.

The Final Details

The final details are the most important because your client wants to leave you with a precision perfect job.

That's why she's paying you to do it for her: because you're the professional and she's not.

For perfect 'detailing', you need an old acrylic brush with a point. You can use polish remover, but I recommend Nail Fresh™ from Creative Nail Design because nothing does this job better. Nail Fresh™ is an ether-based product and evaporates quickly enough never to make the polish go gooey or smear.

In my opinion, polish corrector pens and cuticle sticks wrapped in cotton are more apt to spoil a good polish than to add the fine details to it. The pens become contaminated with polish as soon as you use them and need constant replacement, and orangewood sticks with cotton fibres make more mess than they prevent.

Detailing is simple! Just dip your brush into Nail Fresh™ or remover, then use the point to gently remove any colour that may be spoiling the nice line you want to create.

Wipe the brush on a tissue before dipping back into the bottle if you have more corrections to do.

You can also remove polish from the skin very quickly and easily with Nail Fresh™.

And there you have it: Perfect Precision Polishing! It doesn't take a lot of extra effort, and it's what keeps clients coming back again and again.

CHAPTER 19: History of Success (1992 - 2005)

I have had the priviledge of playing a part in the success of the following.
I'm proud to present to you my winners!

1992 The Nail Show – 1st Place Tip & Overlay	Lynette Allen
1993 The Nail Show – 1st Place Tip & Overlay	Aysha Butt
1993 London Nail Advantage – 1st Place Fibreglass	Ketan Patel
1993 Leeds Hilton Nail Show – 1st Place Tip & Overlay	Beverley Loftus
1994 Leeds Hilton Nail Show – 1st Place Tip & Overlay	Claire Menzies
1996 Olympia – 1st Place Tip & Overlay	Ketan Patel
1997 GMex – 1st Place Tip and Overlay	Debbie Dickson
1998 Olympia – I.N.A. Photographic Competition – 1st Place Winner	Ketan Patel
1998 Olympia – Winner of Winners	Ketan Patel
1998 Olympia – 1st Place Tip & Overlay	Debbie Dickson
1998 Düsseldorf – International 1st Place Winner	Ketan Patel
1998 Midland Nail Event Rookie Competition – 1st Place Tip & Overlay	Marianne Manley
1999 Brighton – 1st Place Tip & Overlay	Ketan Patel
1999 Nail News – British Nail Technician of the Year	Ketan Patel
1999 Olympia – 1st Place Tip & Overlay	Ketan Patel
1999 Olympia – Winner of Winners	Ketan Patel
1999 GMex – 1st Place Tip & Overlay	Diane Plummer

2000 Olympia – 1st Place Tip & Overlay	Liza Smith
2000 Olympia – Winner of Winners	Ketan Patel
2001 Brighton – 1st Place Tip & Overlay	Liza Smith
2001 Brighton – British Nail Technician of the Year	Liza Smith
2001 Olympia – 1st Place Tip & Overlay	Jane Cook
2001 GMex Nail Art Competition – 1st Place Winner	Amanda Reevel
2001 ExCeL – 1st Place Tip & Overlay	Liza Smith
2002 Alternative Nail Awards – Creative on the Edge – 1st Place Winner	Amanda Reevell
2002 Olympia – 1st Place Tip & Overlay	Sarah Walker
2002 GMex – 1st Place Tip & Overlay	Marianne Manley
2002 Las Vegas Nail Olympics – Gold Medal 'Airbrushing' Winner	Jacqui Jefford
2003 Cosmobelleza Spain – 1st Place Tip & Overlay	Joannalea Carlisle
2003 Olympia – Winner of Winners	Liza Smith
2003 SAC Dublin Beauty Show – 1st Place Tip & Overlay	Marina Egan
2003 Spring Salon Show – 1st Place Fiberglass (Fabric#)	Joan Witter
2003 ExCeL – 1st Place Tip & Overlay	Marco Benito
2004 British Beauty – 1st Place Fantasy Nail Art	Jacqui Jefford
2004 Olympia – 1st Place Fiberglass – (Fabric#)	Ruth Fordham
2004 Professional Beauty Awards – Nail Technician of the Year	Marco Pagliuca
2004 I.B.P.A. – Best Natural Nail Technician	Karen O'Niell
2004 I.B.P. Competition – 1st Place – BRISA Gel	Marina Egan
2004 Scottish Beauty – 1st Place – Fiberglass (Fabric#)	Joan Witter

2004 GMEX – 1st Place – Tip & Overlay	Liza Smith
2005 ExCeL – Competitor of the Year (CND Retention+ & Perfect Powders)	Liza Smith
2005 ExCeL – Joint 2nd Place Sculpting (CND Retention+ & Perfect Powders)	Liza Smith
2005 ExCeL – 1st Place Gel (CND Brisa Gels)	Diane Plummer

personal notes

personal notes

personal notes

personal notes

personal notes

personal notes